Think an

1 Where does the water in the pond come from?

2 What animals live in or near the pond?

3 How does the weather change?

4 Why do the animals worry when the pond gets smaller?

5 Why do you think the animals like their new home?

 When the Seasons Change Fold a sheet of paper into four parts. Write the name of a season at the top of each part. Draw what you would wear in that season. Show something you would do.

 School-Home Connection Read aloud the story to a family member. Talk about where the water for your home comes from.

Word Count: 164

EMERGENT READER

EARLY READER

FLUENT READER

ISBN 0-15-323016-9

90000>

9 780153 230165

Sing for the King

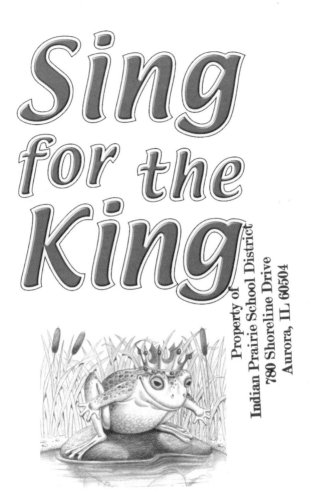

by Shirley Frederick

illustrated by Wendy Rasmussen

Harcourt

Orlando   Boston   Dallas   Chicago   San Diego

Visit The Learning Site!
www.harcourtschool.com

Drip, drop. Two drops come
down. The drops go into the
pond. The pond grows with
every drip.

2

The fish and the tadpoles eat.
A plump tadpole is the king.
Everyone sings!

Sing, sing
for the Tadpole King!
Ring, ring
for the luck he brings!

4

Bring a gift—
a little thing.
Sing a song,
to the Tadpole King!

The sun is hot. The pond gets
small. Now the plants are too
small to eat.

The plants are gone. No
one can run from the sun.
The Tadpole King will help.

Sing, sing
for the Tadpole King!
Ring, ring
for the help he'll bring!

8

Bring a gift—
a little thing.
Sing a song
for the Tadpole King!

9

Then the king looks at his
body. "My tail is gone! I can
hop! Come with me!"

Sing, sing
for the Tadpole King!
Come, sing thanks
for everything!

Bring your gifts
with fang or wing,
and sing a song
to your Frog King!